D1591768

HEALING VISIONS

AN ANTHOLOGY OF MICRO PROSE AND FINE ART PHOTOGRAPHY

Healing Visions © Matter Press and Meg Boscov 2023
All rights reserved
First Matter Press Edition, 2023

ISBN: 978-0-9992529-0-1

Cover and interior design by Michele Charles Barnes
Text set in Adobe Caslon Pro

No part of this book may be reproduced or transmitted in any form or by any means, electronic or mechanical, including photocopying or recording, or by any information storage and retrieval system without permission in writing from the publisher.

MATTER PRESS
PO Box 704
Wynnewood, PA 19096
www.matterpress.com

FOR THE FIGHT TO PROTECT AND SUPPORT

WOMEN'S RIGHTS EVERYWHERE

TABLE OF CONTENTS

TABLE OF CONTENTS CONTINUED

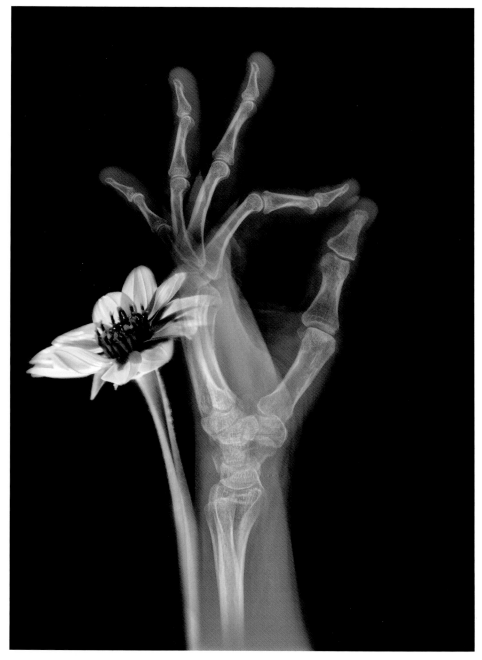

Strange Finding

INTRODUCTION: HEALING VISIONS

"Over time," explains *The Mayo Clinic Guide to Fibromyalgia*, "the brain starts to think that ordinary sensations, such as a light touch, hurt." With this condition (known as central sensitization) "it's as though no one shut off the light switch—or in this case, your nerves—that are telling your brain about the pain." The nerves fire, one after another, constantly, telling the brain that you are in pain, injured, "causing you to feel [the pain] over and over again."

It's invisible, the condition, to the eye, on the blood test, the MRI, the CT scan, the X-ray. If it's invisible, yes, it must all be in your head. You aren't really sick. You just want attention. You are the only one who can see it, feel it, experience it, you and your fellow sufferers. It's just stress. You're just tired. You're just repressed. You're just angry. You need a vacation.

There's only one answer to that: *&%! you. There is no vacation. The pain is real. There's no way to stop the nerves from sending the messages, no way to stop the brain from answering, no way to stop the resulting pain.

How's that for a healing vision?

This is a photograph of Meg's hand, a beginning of that journey toward understanding her pain, a normal X-ray, no sign of anything troublesome, but it's there, the sensitized nerves, invisible, but there, screaming.

Sometimes you look and you cannot see. If a nerve fires in a hand and no one is there to see it...

There is no instrument yet invented to see fibromyalgia. Yet it exists. It makes a sound, sends its messages of pain, of injury, numbness, headache, fog, fatigue.

There is such pain in that hand, those wrists. Can you feel it?—even though you cannot see it?

In the face of pain, writes Viktor Frankl, is "the opportunity for Tragic Optimism—an optimism in the face of uncontrollable suffering; an optimism that ignites the 'defiant power of the human spirit.'"

If fate is the world given to us—the death, the genes, the chronic pain—then perhaps destiny is the choices we make given such a world.

The hand holds a flower.
Of all things.

Fifty-two writers were each given one of Meg's photographs and the "simple" request to write exactly 100 words of prose around the theme of "healing visions." The photograph's title could or could not be used as the prose piece's title; the piece itself could be fiction, creative nonfiction, or neither. What follows are the healing visions of these inspirational writers.

Imagine, stuffed into the coffin-like MRI tube, the walls pressing, the machine pounding, instead of deep primal fear, you have a vision: a dahlia appears like the bright points of stars. Instead of fear and panic, your mind builds to a finale of peace and healing, a display of light, torches alit, synapses firing over and over, each one a new flower, a gardenia, a poppy, an ethereal nigella. Instead of flight, your mind wants you to stay. Instead of turning on you, your mind envisions what might save you.

I cannot imagine such a thing. For me, Randall Brown, writing this introduction, there's mostly the fear, the panic, the flight, the MRI the embodiment of the worst: entrapment, death, imprisonment, fate. But for Meg Boscov, our photographer and artist, that vision above actually happened. Her mind arose with a dream-like vision, a vision to soothe, a healing vision.

It wasn't luck. Meg arrived at that place through work, the work of mindfulness, meditation, therapeutic Zoom sessions, a journey through the chronic pain of fibromyalgia, a pain particularly felt in the hands and wrists, felt mostly when taking and working on, of all things, photographs. Her passion. Her artistic dreams. Her love.

Matter Press' first book of Meg's photographs hit the world right at the same time as COVID-19 did, and we decided to donate the books to anyone sick or quarantined, as a way to provide a bit of help during a horrific time. Five hundred people asked for and received a copy of the first book, HAND-IN-HAND. No one, I'm sure, had any idea that two years later, the world would wobble on its still-sick journey toward what exactly? That is the question, yes? Toward what?

Can you imagine it's building toward beauty? Toward a finale of brightness? Toward shining? Toward healing? Toward the good?

Here we all are, stuffed into this ever-terrifying world, the walls pressing. What might arise to save us? We hope that something here might help you not only stay, but thrive.

Healing Vision

Echoed

12

LIFE

Roberta Allen

Suddenly Life, with a capital L, was perfect. Everything in its rightful place. Wasn't this the "Large Mind?" As compared to the small mind of ordinary, everyday existence. How can this be? she asked herself, though she knew then that Life was larger than wars, than plagues, than natural disasters. But in the faintest corner where the everyday persisted came a thought: *What if I never come back to the small mind?* Wasn't the everyday mind also the place where she knew many joys, apart from the fears, the frustrations, the anger, the sadness. Suddenly, the Large Mind was gone.

Testing the Waters

OUR OWN SELVES

Kathi Appelt

"For goodness sake," they said. And you reached out. Your finger's tip touched mine. God touched Adam, said, "Get on with your own selves." In my land, the church ladies smirk, "bless her, she just can't help herself." Gazing into the pond like that, like no one could be more fucking lovely. As if beauty carried shame in its pocket, a hole for a stone to slip through. In the forest, an echo, "come to me, my honey pie, my sugar plum, my sweet Baboo." Can't you see? We have our own Sistine Chapel, caught in the moon's melted puddle.

Demeter

REUNION

Sybil Baker

On the Turkish coast, my mother plays with her grandson in a pool surrounded by lime trees. Across the road under a sun as bright as a daffodil, a farmer bales hay cut by an ancient tractor. A few months ago in this country, archeologists discovered the ruins of an altar site for Demeter, mother-goddess of grain. When her daughter Persephone was abducted to the underworld, Demeter's sorrow killed the earth's harvest. Only after Persephone returned was earth reborn. What is an altar for? Salvation or sacrifice? Perhaps it is for this: a child swimming into openhearted arms, world abloom.

The Blue Escape

JUST LIKE THAT

Robin Black

The color embraced her, that morning. Blue. It held her, and her memories vanished. Every worry drifted away. The sun spread out in the water.

Years pass, but all her life, at times of stress she closes her eyes and conjures the color (lonely moments, bereavement days) and she feels the buoying blue all around her, warm as her own blood. Caring for her.

(Years later, when she is old, her daughter will ask where she goes when her lids lower *just like that*.)

In the distance, there are others, talking, laughing. She forgets them, forgets about herself. She breathes.

Primeval

CONQUERING THE DARKNESS

Ellen Boscov

When night is missing moon, Junior Mouse cries, "Mother, can what shined so dear disappear?" Off he runs past Spider's legs and web of steely leaves. The heavens swirl with cattail seeds. The crickets buzz. His ankle from some prickle bleeds. Still, he scales a wall and into window squeezes. Perched on tabletop, through silver fuzz of tears, he spies the holy wheel of light. With cheesy bite, he verifies, "It's moon alright!" Victorious, our mouse returns to nest of mother's arms and shares, "The moon's nearby." "I see," Mother sighs, while gazing at the sphere in Junior's brilliant eye.

Eventide

EVENTIDE

Kristin Burcham

Spring Break, 1987. Fort Lauderdale? South Padre? Nah, my best friend and I ventured, giggling in hammocks with Cayman breezes. First tastes of lobster in melted sunshine butter, fancy wine we struggled to pronounce. Slapdash sunscreen, like two reckless encounters with island boys—oh, the triumphant retellings over patio breakfast, wide-eyed wonderment of each other's daring!

Nowadays we call across miles to confide our aging bodies' latest treachery. Ailments. Diagnoses. Disheartening prognoses. And yet—always—we giggle, for time can't submerge what we still see: our younger selves, as clear beneath the years as tanned limbs and floating hair beneath the Caribbean blue.

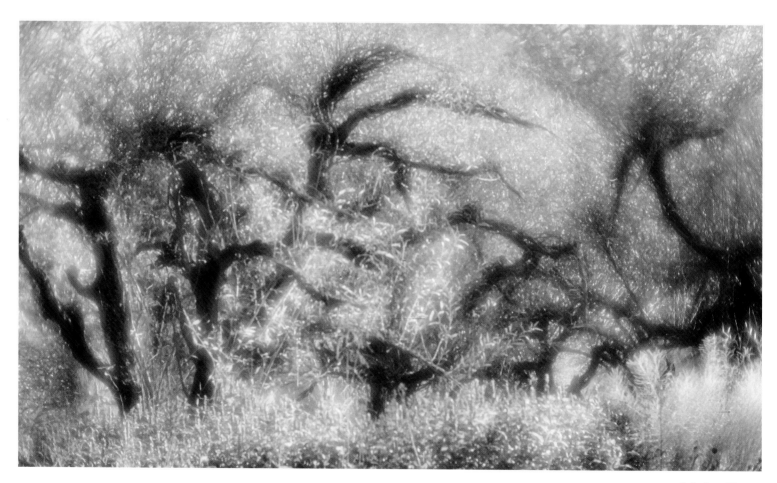

Modern Dance

FOREST LIFE

Bonnie Jo Campbell

Dance while you're part of the understory, flexible and uncertain of survival. Once you become a great tree, once the life of the forest depends on you, your dance becomes a deliberation of inches. Wind berates you from above, but it will take human lifetime of growing moss to bow down enough to extend to the leaf litter a limb that cannot be retracted. Such a branch, once released, decays, becomes a gift to the life below. A laborious dance of self-sacrifice. Similarly, kindness in youth can be simple, sweet; later, kindness is often the kindness of the sharp knife.

Saguaro Reach

SAGUARO FUTURE

Tara Campbell

And still they reach upward, ribs raised toward the sun, dowsing the sky for light; striving even at night toward brightness, spines craving moonglow, the pin-prick of stars; despite nicks and bumps, diversions, false starts, all arcs bending toward freedom above. And even while moving apart, the arms rise, gifting each other more space to grow. What would it mean to sprout on our own unique paths, thriving, divided yet balanced on one common stalk? What might it feel like to cherish our own spines on other faces, celebrate the flowering of our alternate selves, sharing expansive and radiant sky?

Pop

THERE'LL SOON BE A TIME WHEN

Sara Siddiqui Chansarkar

your breasts will stop leaking, the corners of your eyes will itch to drip. Your stomach will growl and you'll stare at the egg tray in the fridge, unsure, but your hands won't tremble when cracking a shell. That day, you'll pry open the hesitant window, let the sun slant in. You'll remove the bib from under your pillow, stow away the squishy squirrel and the battery bongo after pressing them to your heart. The next day, you'll scatter seeds to invite robins for nesting. Finally, you'll cry when a swollen bud breaks and a sliver of purple peeks out.

Ease & Peace

EASE AND PEACE

Mare Chapman

In these dark and painfully tumultuous times where what seemed secure is unraveling, finding ease and peace is vital. It's our sacred responsibility now. By pausing to reflect deeply on the water lily, rising from its long root in the dark murky primal mud, its beautiful flower opening joyfully to the light above, we can rest our battered minds, hearts, bodies, and spirits for a time. And since we're all connected, our individual well-being ripples out and affects others in all directions. Let's meditate on the water lily and strengthen our inner ease and peace.

Swept Up

DESTINY'S CHILD

By Elaine Chiew

Magnolia, do you know all the ways to say the color purple? You dream of being the starlet amidst a line-up of sage and eucalyptus, laurel spray and baby's breath. Oh honey, what makes you special is the way you unfurl yourself to the sun. Allium, salvia, sweet rocket, they do not compare. Lift up your head: who says your destiny is the vase and not the field? Do not despair, do not hunger for what you can never be. Here in a sea of fluttering purple, you are blazingly alive. Recognise that when the secateurs come, the wounding begins.

Summer Soloist

MY INHERITANCE

Kim Chinquee

As the daffodils in my yard begin to die, new flowers come forth. Tulips. Solomons Seal. Lilacs. Before all of these were snowdrops.

It's only my second spring in my new home.

I have to take down a diseased sugar maple. It leaves a big scar in the front of my yard. I plant a Rose of Sharon.

The original owners were horticulturalists; this is my inheritance. As old flowers fade and die, yet new kinds come forth. There are lilies, ferns, roses.

I do my best to nurture them. I do my best to get rid of the weeds.

Pleasure Garden

PRAYER FOR SAINT FIACRE

Debra Di Blasi

Give us back the times we turned from the sun as color fell from gardens otherwise brightly hued. Times when mourning doves slept, like us, with one eye open, cradled in broken arms of oaks. Give us back the bloom of our cheeks, swelling breasts, lilies lit in irises of welling eyes. And beyond the hedge and shadow waiting: a field of black-eyed Susans where we kissed naked, legs tangled as bittersweet vines. Night came always falling then, not felled. Forgiving Saint, give us back the years lost to easy despair. We promise this time to make time stand still.

Hellebore Cocktail

HELLEBORE COCKTAIL

Pietra Dunmore

It is what it is. The image to present to the masses. Hair coiffed into place. Eyeliner applied with precision. The trick is to gaze at the bridge of the nose. The look is like music, jazz—a red lip, a winged line on the eye. I'm cheerful and ambitious. Communication with my face. No words allowed. This is my painted encouragement, my self-love in colorful strokes. My punctuation without a sentence. With a last look in the mirror, I tell myself I am confident, I am certain, I am amazing. I smile because today I will conquer the world.

Love in the Clouds

THE HANDSOME DOCTOR WITH CLASPED HANDS PLACED DELIBERATELY ON THE DESK BEFORE HIM

Kathy Fish

and wearing a small, though not unkind smile, said: Maybe your chronic debilitating pain is due to depression.

The fifty-something peri-menopausal woman with a pet ferret and a lover who openly cheated on her replied: Maybe not.

It seemed a miracle was in order. Only yesterday, she'd read that scientists were able to build a functioning human heart from a spinach leaf.

She told the doctor, who gave his own two hands a squeeze but said nothing. Healing, she realized then, was a matter of conviction and self-interest. Of deciding who could stay and who must go.

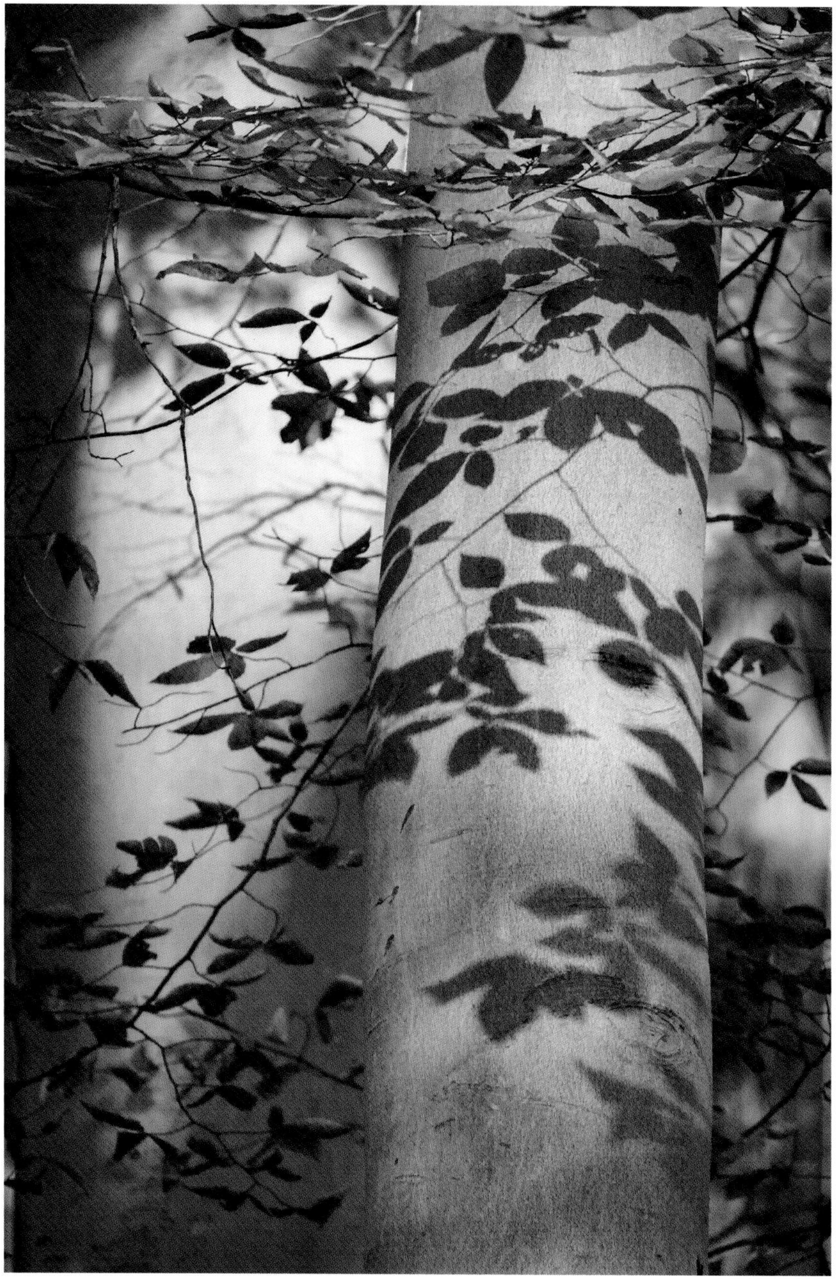

November Beech

LIGHT AND SHADOW

Sherrie Flick

The early morning light untangled Kris from her bedsheets. She'd unplugged the alarm clock the night before in order to eliminate the bright red numbers that marked her days. Today was timeless. She'd decided in advance. The little dog curled at the end of the bed thumped its little tail when he heard her rustle. The sunlight was clear and bright against her bedroom wall. Kris felt she could swim right through it down the stairs. She knew the tree outside her kitchen window waited with open arms, had already decided its leaves were perfect in both light and shadow.

Intoxicating

NEIGHBORS

Molly Gaudry

On the news, stories of people banging pots and pans from their balconies, strangers singing from rooftops, all to praise the doctors and nurses in their own communities and around the world. And another video—about an elderly man who daily played the piano in remembrance of his wife. The video was made by one of his neighbors who happened to also play the piano; and it was about how they played together now, these strangers in their solitude, never seeing one another, just playing songs through their walls and open windows, every day reaching right into each other's hearts.

Reed Song

BARE

Amina Gautier

They go outside to keep from saying things they won't be able to take back. It's not the questions—they're glad their mother is asking, is trying, is making the effort. Their mother asks, "What is a dead name? Did I give you one?" She delights in taking the blame, gobbling it up and licking her lips, eager for more. She wants to know their new name, but the name isn't new—just excavated, uncovered, finally revealed. Outside, in their mother's yard, they announce it, introducing themselves to the night, the moon, and a tree's two naked branches, hanging bare.

Annual Party

STRAY

Carol Guess

Sunlit poppies, carnations, roses that prickle your throat until breathing stings. Birds singing an untranslatable song. The word *bird* all wrong, as if one bird was just like the others. The high-pitched sound you can't hear that sets the dog crying. How *dog* is also wrong. How your name never fit: the blandest name they knew. Their gift. There are a thousand ways to love and still be wrong about a name. This dog won't run to the name you call; too many names in too many shelters. She never comes, solves the problem in silence. Never leaves your side.

Fringe

AT THE CORNER OF RESENTMENT AND CURIOSITY

Watsuki Harrington

Where did the man end and the myth begin? Who was my biological father who gave pocket Bibles to Vietnam Vets rather than raise me, his only daughter? What part of him did I have too? I had to see for myself. At the edge of unknowing, before I knew his scent: part-coconut, part-must; and the funny way he slurred his Rs; when I could have chosen anything, but where two roads clearly laid. I chose curiosity. Softened my gaze to see more than speak. I slowed the critic inside. Through humility, love pools like a glistening mirage.

Twilight Flight

AQUILEGIA

Tama Janowitz

When the flowers floated, smiling, from the sky, the temperature was already a hundred. Overheated, the columbines sagged, covering everything in bruised blue tissue—just one more difficulty in that neighborhood, which already had issues. Now, nobody could see the airless streets, melting asphalt padded with flower skin. The residents ripped holes in the petal curtains, devoured the draperies, stuffing their mouths. Stamens, hooked overhead, shed swollen pollen. Leaning out the windows, no one could stop themselves from grabbing handfuls, biting yellow tennis ball fluff. "What's going on?" occurred to everyone around the same time, suddenly munching more slowly.

Spring House

HEALING VISION

Lisa Diane Kastner

As children we had hid among darkened pockets of the forest frequented by those who had Crossed. We reveled in their stories under vibrant stars. In the Winters we had curled up to fires deep inside their home. Now I gently knock on the same Local's door. Days since he passed, my heart quivered between grieving and relief. His distress finally over. From behind the red frame come footsteps. I breathe deeply as the doorknob turns and exhale as it creaks open to reveal … my love. Now of The Crossing. He whispers, "Come in, my Love. I'm still here."

The Getaway

BERRIES

Beth Kephart

Then I went out hunting for their percolated color—their carmine red, their orpiment orange, their gamboge yellow, their great emerald hiding in the bushes. I didn't need much, or many. I didn't mind them old or withered. I didn't pluck them, I didn't steal them, I would never eat them, but in that darkest season, the brilliant baubles of the autumn berries became a kind of reason. The rough hands of the wind couldn't reach them. Nor the greed of the fat-cheeked squirrels. Nor the pokes of the birds. The berries were mine. I defied the season with them.

Yet All Awake

YET ALL AWAKE

Tara Laskowski

We move in the darkest of summer nights. The moon our guide. It's slow, the progress—sometimes we march, sometimes we sway, sometimes we get blown off course and wither, brittle as dried cornstalk.

But still, we come.

Are we flowers? Fragile, bending to whatever whim? Rooted and fixed and resigned?

Or are we ghosts? Relentless. Haunting, stalking, thirsty for revenge? Biding our time in the shadows behind the shadow.

We've always been here. We always will be. Flowers. Ghosts. Dreams. Nightmares.

Listen quietly as we sigh. Wait as we awake. Watch, forever, as we rise and bloom and roar.

Flora

THERE'S A GREEN WORLD ON MY WALL

Diane Lefer

Forest green, shamrock and jade, evergreen, moss, and shades of green that I can't name, and a tint so pale it fades to white. A woodland scene painted by the cousin I never knew. Estranged for his violent psychosis, condemned, gay. So much turmoil in his mind and lately in mine. When outrage boils over and vision blurs, his canvas with its cool beauty reminds me: He knew rejection, dark visions, rage, but also the pond through a scrim of mist. My wavering faith needs this. He saw lily pads, a streak of sunlight, and this too, sky and trees.

Sonoran Trip

THE MOMENT BEFORE

Jo-Ann Mapson

Just before the migraine lifts there is a silverblue flash and then come the overlapping images, as rapid as automatic gunfire.

Cactusmountainskycloudlightningcactusmountainskycloudlighting.

A migraine hurts so differently than other pain that the best thing is pressing your forehead onto the Saltillo tile. Yet the ER doc with the silver syringe is the answer. A sting, then you feel every bone in your face give up the muscles they had been clinging to. You sigh, grateful as prayer. Then comes the quickening in the body, knitting everything together again. Saying: Oh, there you are, Self. Gather up, and do let's continue.

The Ocher

OCHRE

Tara Lynn Masih

Cantabria, Spain, 20,000 BCE

Girl holds what is not baby anymore. Her keening echoes. She dips her finger in clay dust. Places it against the cave wall where she sleeps. One more mark, rusty-red, to show pain. The love of something not fully realized, just dawning.

Gloucester, Massachusetts, 2022

During the plein-air class, her breath quickens as she finds just the right blend of ochre and burnt sienna to complete the sunset wash above the sea's horizon. In that perfect brush stroke, fear and anger fall away. Just paper, salt, fish-scented breeze, time stretching beyond where the world falls away.

Beach Day

BEACH DAY

Patricia McConnell

Fun. Flippy. Flirty. Frivolous. How could you? How could I? When the world is on fire, and yet flooded over? When your heart has broken, or your body betrays you? How could we run on the beach, lie down in the meadow, let the juice of a bright-red watermelon run down our chins? Because we have to. Because joy and sanity live in a single daisy. Or the scent of your dog's paws. Because the tiniest things have the power to heal us. We just have to be able to find them. They are out there, always, waiting for us.

Destination Unknown

REMEMBERING MARILYN

Ellen Meister

"Will you marry me?" he asked, forgetting she had answered that question more than sixty-five years ago. Forgetting the baking heat of that June day, the white tulle of his bride's dress, the kosher chicken served on gold-rimmed plates. Forgetting the one-two-three of the waltz, the honeymoon in Saranac Lake, the ceremony of his son's bris, where he fainted before the Rabbi even finished. He forgot his second child, a saucer-eyed girl, and a third, unplanned—his bonus daughter. Also the house, the business, this beautiful woman's name.

She smiled gently. "Of course."

He sobbed and took her hand. "Marilyn."

70

Becoming

BECOMING

Kristine Ong Muslim

Something always feels right about this place, even if it reminds you of all the times you lied and said yes when asked if you were okay. The breeze, the calm, the branches heavy with white wildflowers brooding and prayerful, their tips touching the water. If time were this lake, then grief is what's reflected on the water's surface, what stays undissolved even as you shake the dust off your ghost towns. There are days when it becomes hard to tell where the wildflowers end and the water begins. Maybe this is how hope takes root, how healing finds you.

Valley Forge

YIELD

Robin Oliveira

Morning, again. Mist a veil, all that is beautiful hidden. We rise, wondering, can I do this again? It is true that our work, our hope, accumulates, the infinitesimal gestures of good will and thoughtfulness we make blundering about in the world, seeking to survive, seeking to give. We bend to plow, plant, nurture, scythe (here is unavoidable pain), and reap. I don't understand, not really, why the pain, why any pain? But later—*after*—and maybe even now because time is a whirling mystery, the obscuring mist parts to reveal the golden life we labored, its bounty of love.

At Long Last

FOR LOVE HER
CENTER HOLDS

Pamela Painter

She first noticed her failing eyesight when hearing Anna Sophie Mutter play Tchaikovsky's Concerto in D with the Boston Symphony. Mutter was the center of the music, at the center of the stage. The orchestra receded on either side and around her, the conductor also a blur.

She described all this in retrospect. Recalled for the eye doctor bending toward her, whose enormous black glasses resembled an insect's eyes. Later, at the beach, one umbrella stood out from the others as if it was waiting for her lover. For her gaze will always be there for the one she loves.

Water Goddess

LAKE

Alina Pleskova

In the workshop, Sophia instructed us to write about the last body of water that we jumped into. She emphasized *jumped*, as distinct from another, safer way. I scan my memory, rewinding until I've gone back too far for my liking. I'm too young to be this risk-averse already. For a long while, my primary use of spare time entailed finding as many different uses for my body as possible. But I've been around long enough to know what can happen unintentionally. What already has. I think of this at the dingy lake, its glimmer nonetheless alluring. I jump.

Mending the Broken

MENDING THE BROKEN

Zalisa Rabin

As a young and hopeful reader of self-help books, I longed to start over. To begin each school year with a crisp, unblemished notebook, a clean slate. Now at fifty-seven, frayed and dog-eared, rife with visible erasures, I look to the strength and beauty of this current form that I inhabit. I vow to feel its health as consciously as I have dwelled in its pain. Today, my sturdy feet carried me up and down the limestone hills of Lisbon. For how long? The only way to be in this body now is to love it fiercely.

Light Therapy

COMPLETE

Victoria Redel

I want to be the bee circling the glossy petal, then a dip in, a slide down the cup, knocking into anthers and coming up pollen dusty. I want to be the tulip, radiant, complete unto itself—male and female tucked within, self-pollinating.

And still the bee I also am flies off woozy, shaking my tulip into another tulip—is that you, beloved?—who receives me though you are also perfect with your pistils, your stamens.

And the wind, let's also both be wind. Carrying seed and water.

Bee and flower and wind. And also, you and you and you.

Musing

THREAT FROM ON HIGH

Trish L. Rodriguez

She faces the assault of the sun, the wind, the rain. The demon approaches with its mouth agape, its wings beating with threatened destruction. At stake—her survival. The flapping could rip her apart. And yet she must confront the terror. Not a weakness, instead her curves force her towards the creature's oppressive, misty breath. Her blooming face remembers the stench of it, the screeching. She doesn't dare to think she won't survive. She turns toward this threat with her face serene and her back straight as an engorged stem on the familial shoulders of those who stood before her.

Forsythia

LET ME BE

Ethel Rohan

a flowered shrub bedded in rich, crawling soil, standing tall yet relaxed. A host of golden in the forest, leaning into warmth, watched over by trees helping the world to breathe, survive.

Giving of my seeds, nectar, sweetness. May I be unpicked, rooted. A blaze of delight, art, glory.

Hello, shimmery supersonic bird.

Take your fill, striped buzzer.

You will not deplete me. For even though parts die, they will again bud, grow, crown, sway. Never knowing before or after.

And so on and on, for your pleasure, for mine, as we go round the fiery up down up sun.

Not a Day Goes By

REAL FIGHTS OVER FAKE FLOWERS

Kathleen Rooney

Last summer, our beloved ruby-throated hummingbird Zum Zum, whose throat is lily-white, hatched out a daughter, Li'l Zum. Notoriously territorial, when they returned this season, at first they were fine, but began having acrobatic airborne battles over the blossoms of the red plastic feeder. Although we got a second ersatz bouquet to broker peace, Li'l Zum defeated her parent triumphantly. Zum Zum retreated, no more to be seen. But. That wasn't the end! Today, Zum Zum's back and so is Li'l Zum and harmony appears restored. We'll never know what healed between them, but now we have two hummingbirds again.

Moon Glow

STRIX

Natasha Sajé

Last week at a party a man lectured her without once looking at her face. She took note of the way he moved his hands and mouth, she tracked his incessant noise. If only humans were more like owls, a genus in which females are larger and more fierce than males. She could have swooped down silently with enormous wings, plucked him up and fed him to her young. It's conflicting things she wants, she knows: to be acknowledged and respected—and to have a camouflage so keen, she can't be seen from rock nor branch nor glowing, flowery field.

Looking for Myself

FOR MEG

Susanna Sonnenberg

We were dark in the woods, two stammering chicks, grounded, and we didn't know the other was near. I thought, *I am alone.* You ruffled faint against the leaves, and I turned my gaze, *What's this?* We admired our small wings, new feathers. You weren't taking pictures yet, and I was barely writing. We made a strong fuss of each other, twined in a dense bramble. Before we named what need we had to be healed, before we spoke the words *thunder, mayhem, escape.* Friend, it is always our season, the lamp in the falling light, the invitation. *Rise up.*

Curtain's Call

AD ME REDEO

C.J. Spataro

This sky is the sea and this curtain a sail. Soon I will escape this confinement. On the far shore of the sky on an island made of clouds, I am waiting for myself. My arms are strong and tanned, and my embrace is sheltering and warm. On this island cloud in the pale blue sky-sea I am safe. I am whole, quiet. The breath of peace fills me. I am invulnerable, yet free. With light feathery wings, I lift myself above the airy ocean and embrace the sun. I leave behind my pillowy curtain sail and soar toward hope.

Morning Glory

WHEN EVERY FLOWER LOOKS LIKE A FALLOPIAN TUBE

Jennifer Steil

I heal myself only at gunpoint. I learned the power of yoga breathing when I was kidnapped while pregnant, desperate not to miscarry. I learned meditation after anxiety forced me into a psychiatric hospital. I don't stop whipping myself forward to achieve until I must. Now, the cells of my body rebel to still me, pin me in place. Their swollen ranks march from ovaries to diaphragm. And suddenly, I'm an optimist. Not from any natural tendency, but because I have a 12-year-old daughter and cannot endure a single moment if I don't believe I will survive to raise her.

Tango

MR. AND MRS. DOCTOR

Wendy Rich Stetson

He is unconscious. Briefly. Long enough to rattle me, though the procedure is planned. I count minutes outside the city-scented hospital. An unwelcome shift as doctor becomes patient. My rock-solid New Englander, heart of gold and mind of granite, the voice of reasoned comfort. Tucked beside him, our spines like sinuous, synchronous stems, I dream while he practices. What luxury to tell stories in the house of a physician. Roots intertwined, we face away, yet always the tickle of tiny hairs whispers, "I'm here." Between sidewalk cracks, I, the Mrs. Doctor, hold my breath and squint into the sun, waiting.

Galaxy

A SAFE PLACE WITH SNACKS

Chelsea Stickle

The pollen-speckled harvest mouse crawls deeper into the mouth of the red tulip. His weight bends the bud horizontal but doesn't break it. The sky turns frightening. He crunches into stamens and pollen scatters across his nose and whiskers. Yellow dust on earthy fur. A long tail circled around. He can wait out the rain. The weather changes constantly. Patience is key. Patience and a safe place with snacks. When the rain stops, he stays in his dry cocoon. He gazes up at the stars. Sees everything there has ever been, everything there ever will be. Then he falls asleep.

Out There

BORN AGAIN

Nancy Stohlman

And then we all became trees: one minute we were walking or driving or scheming or daydreaming and the next minute we were trees, oaks and willows and pine trees, and the highway was trees, and sidewalks were trees, and bicycles were trees, and some wished they'd been next to family or picked a better view or gotten out of this damn office, forever beside colleagues all realizing the same thing, and who instinctively began to reach branches to the other as they'd never done in real life, leaves reaching for leaves as we all turned towards the sun.

STILL ME

Julia Strayer

After the stroke, my mother's brain is a bird that circles inside a barn. Sometimes finding light through wallboard cracks or a door flung open on sunny days, but mostly just fluttering endless loops in semi-darkness, trying to locate what was lost.

She remembers I'm her daughter, but not where I live. Sometimes believes I'm her sister and forgets where she lives.

We go for lunch. She invites an elderly man alone to join us, helps with his coat, reminds him he's important.

She circles, sometimes catching her reflection. Even if she forgets everything, she still remembers who she is.

104

Desert Muse

DESERT MUSE

Jillian Sullivan

Rising in the dawn light, sharpness and pain. How bearable they are under the gentle reckoning of sky. Time to contemplate, assimilate, accept that light flaring on each tissued angle. In surge, or upthrust, a blazing into consciousness: despair, evasion, righteousness, rejection, sadness, aloneness. Aloneness, brightness, acknowledgement, delight, humility, openness.

I am tramping across the scoria slope of the mountain. Each careful boot-fall wedged into the shifting stones. And there are the plants, their thorn-tipped blades, their fine-leafed stoic-ness. On a rock, the tan fluidity of lizard who knows how to live here. In the blue above, a skylark soars.

Carefree

SHAKE THE DARK

Girija Tropp

Forget being sixty-five, be twenty-five, travelling, drinking ouzo at some festival outside Athens, and going home with some Darth Veda whose feet hang off the edge of the bed, and compare the American to the Greek hunk; compare ordinary flu to COVID19 while bringing to mind a dress bought at a touristy Venetian market, lace-trimmed uneven panels reaching to V up the bodice, and how it disappeared around the time of the movie buff, a twenty-nine-year-old male appearing and exiting through the bay window of the bedroom. He was a karate master, and I enjoyed the spectacular.

Unidentified

THE NEXT GUARDIAN

Deb Olin Unferth

Once installed, his life secretly expanded. He watched the lizards scoot through the sand, and the insects and small animals. They couldn't be out much after dawn, when the ozone concentration rose, but that was fine, and he picked over the rocks by night, found the tiny ghostly desert flowers, came inside when the sun lifted over the orange horizon. And the sky! It was everything he had hoped for, the satellites humming and moving through the night. The one somewhat disappointing part was the humans, so loud and desperate and mean. He disposed of the few that were left.

Nigella on the Half-Shell

NIGELLA ON THE HALF-SHELL

Liza Gardner Walsh

Lately, each night, her dreams were of strings, cords, lines. A kite string dancing beyond view.

Her dad's fishing line dipping into the reservoir off his rusted dinghy. Her grandmother's amber necklace, still warm from wear.

Helpful, friendly lines. Strings tied to positive times, benign moments. It was a relief to feel hitched at night as her untethered days flew by, the world deeply adrift. Her heart more fragile. Ready to rip at the slightest storm.

Each day, she pictured those lines, gripped them with might, her head held high. Undeterred by the world's waves. Cupped in her own light.

Beacon

THE SURVIVOR

Cat Warren

Common horsetail grew and spread near the creek. Their segmented purple and green stalks, tipped with delicate strobili, pushed up through gravel and mud. They meant spring, cold, wet tennis shoes—and solitude.

Beyond the horsetail thicket lay a water hole. There, come summer, crawfish madly skulled backward, escaping no matter how carefully I stalked them.

For 350 million years, *Equisetum* has survived in poor soil, thrived where other plants withered, spread its spores on the wind, pushed its rhizomes deep underground. Once a giant that fed hadrosaurs, down by the creek where I grew up, it fed my soul.

L'heure Bleue

ROOT, ROOT, ROOT

Xu Xi 許素細

Season of sun and baseball. Home team, New York Mets, doing okay. We root around Apps, seeking each live game. Today Spectrum, tomorrow SNY, the day after Apple TV. The way of the world on AI and this summer there's never any good news so our eternal game is the healing-est vision, salve for sanity, even if red glares the horror of the country right now. My adopted country. I pledged allegiance to a democracy for equality and baseball. Come on America, still counting on you. One, two, please America, truth and real lives matter. Stay in the game. Please.

AUTHOR BIOS

Roberta Allen has authored nine books, including *The Princess of Herself*, one of three very short and short story collections, a novella, a novel, a memoir and, among three writing guides, *Fast Fiction*. She is also a conceptual artist in the collections of The Met and MoMA. The Smithsonian Archives of American Art have acquired her art papers.

Kathi Appelt lives in Texas with her husband and four cats. She has written books and other stuff for toddlers to adults. She likes awards. She's won a few. But they're not why she writes. Ask her what is new, and she will probably begin with something old.

Sybil Baker's latest novel *Apparitions* is forthcoming from Signal8Press in 2023. A professor at the University of Chattanooga, she lives in Calhoun, Georgia. Learn more at sybilbaker.net.

Robin Black is the author of a story collection, *If I loved you, I would tell you this*; a novel, *Life Drawing*; an essay collection, *Crash Course: Essays From Where Writing and Life Collide*; and the harder to categorize, memoirish appreciation of and conversation with a book, *Mrs. Dalloway, Bookmarked* (Ig Publishing, 2022). Robin lives in NYC and Pennsylvania with her husband and daughter and dog. www.robinblack.net

Ellen Boscov is a writer, composer, and actor. She wrote the screenplay and score for the short film *First Light*, a 2021 AAFF Academy Award®-qualifying Film Festival winner. Her full-length plays have been produced in NYC and SF. Ellen has acted in indie films, theaters, and improv comedy clubs.

Kristin Burcham received her MFA from Vermont College of Fine Arts. She has been published across multiple genres and helps her 7th grade English students to discover themselves as readers and writers.

Bonnie Jo Campbell is the bestselling author of *Mothers, Tell Your Daughters, Once Upon a River*, and *American Salvage*, among other works. She was a National Book Award finalist and a Guggenheim Fellow, winner of the 2019 Mark Twain Award. She is six foot tall and rides a donkey.

Tara Campbell is a writer, teacher, Kimbilio Fellow, fiction co-editor at *Barrelhouse*, and graduate of American University's MFA. Publication credits include *SmokeLong Quarterly, Masters Review, Wigleaf, Strange Horizons*, and *CRAFT Literary*. She's the author of a novel and four multi-genre collections including her newest, *Cabinet of Wrath: A Doll Collection*.

Sara Siddiqui Chansarkar is an Indian American writer. A technologist by profession and a writer by passion, she is the author of *Morsels of Purple* and *Skin Over Milk*. She is a Prose Editor at *Janus Literary* and a Submissions Editor at *SmokeLong Quarterly*. More at https://saraspunyfingers.com. Reach her @PunyFingers.

Mare Chapman, M.A., mindfulness-based feminist psychotherapist, teacher, author, is devoted to helping women find freedom from internalized misogyny through mindfulness to live fully empowered lives. Her book, *Unshakeable Confidence, the Freedom to be Our Authentic Selves: Mindfulness for Women*, is based on the class she's taught for 25 years. www.marechapman.com.

Elaine Chiew is the author of *The Heartsick Diaspora* and editor/compiler of *Cooked Up: Food Fiction From Around the World*. Twice winner of the Bridport Prize, her stories have been anthologized in the UK, US and Asia. In 2022, she was Guest Editor for Best Small Fictions.

Kim Chinquee is the author of seven fiction collections; her debut novel, *Pipette*, was published in Fall 2022 with Ravenna Press. Her work has been published widely and received three Pushcart Prizes and a Henfield Prize. She is Senior Editor of *New World Writing Quarterly*, Contributing Editor of *Midwest Review,* and an associate professor of English at SUNY-Buffalo State University. She's a triathlete and lives with her three dogs in Tonawanda, NY.

Debra Di Blasi (www.debradiblasi.com) is an artist and award-winning author of 11 books, with prose, poetry and hybrids published in anthologies of innovative literature and in prominent journals. Her newest novel, *Birth of Eros*, was published November 2022 by Kernpunkt Press.

Pietra Dunmore writes short stories, creative nonfiction, and poetry. Her writing has appeared in *Hippocampus Magazine*, *Philadelphia Stories*, *The Naisona*, and *Santa Fe Writers Project Quarterly*. You can read her work on www.pietradunmore.net.

Kathy Fish's stories have most recently appeared in *Ploughshares, Wigleaf,* and *Washington Square Review.* Her work has been widely anthologized, notably in the *Norton Reader, Best Small Fictions*, and *Best American Nonrequired Reading.* She is a recipient of the *Copper Nickel* Editors' Prize and a Ragdale Foundation Fellowship.

Sherrie Flick is the author of the novel *Reconsidering Happiness* and two short story collections, *Whiskey, Etc.* and *Thank Your Lucky Stars.* She is a senior editor at *SmokeLong Quarterly,* served as series editor for *The Best Small Fictions 2018,* and is co-editor for the W. W. Norton anthology *Flash Fiction America.*

Molly Gaudry is the founder of Lit Pub and the author of *We Take Me Apart*, which was a finalist for the Asian American Literary Award and shortlisted for the PEN/Osterweil. She teaches creative writing at Stony Brook University.

Amina Gautier is the author of three short story collections: *At-Risk, Now We Will Be Happy*, and *The Loss of All Lost Things.* She is the recipient of the Blackwell Prize, the Chicago Public Library Foundation's 21st Century Award, and the PEN/MALAMUD Award for Excellence in the Short Story.

Carol Guess is the author of twenty books of poetry and prose, including *Doll Studies: Forensics* and *Tinderbox Lawn.* Her short fiction collection *Sleep Tight Satellite* is forthcoming in 2023 from Tupelo Press. She is Professor of English at Western Washington University, where she teaches Queer Studies and Creative Writing.

Watsuki found her homeless, Bible-preaching, biological father when she was twenty-two and is currently writing a book about that adventure. Her work has appeared in journals and chapbooks. She has an MFA in Creative Writing and lives in the Philadelphia area.

Tama Janowitz is the author of 12 books—novels, short stories, non-fiction, sci-fi, children, including stories purchased by Andy Warhol for a film, then made by Merchant-Ivory. Her awards include two National Endowment in Fiction, Alfred Hodder Fellow at Princeton, and New York Foundation for the Arts.

Lisa Diane Kastner is the founder of Running Wild and RIZE Presses. Featured in *Forbes,* she's been named to Yahoo Finance's Top 10 Entrepreneurs to Watch in 2021, and named to New York Weekly's Top Ten Females to Watch in 2021.

Beth Kephart is the award-winning author of three-dozen books in multiple genres, co-founder of Juncture Workshops, and a book artist. Her new books are *Wife | Daughter | Self: A Memoir in Essays* and *We Are the Words: The Master Memoir Class.* More at bethkephartbooks.com.

Tara Laskowski is the award-winning author of the suspense novels *One Night Gone* and *The Mother Next Door.* She also wrote two short story collections, *Bystanders* and *Modern Manners For Your Inner Demons.* She was the long-time editor of *SmokeLong Quarterly* and lives in Virginia. Follow her on Twitter and Instagram @TaraLWrites.

Diane Lefer's published work includes books, stories, and advocacy journalism. Please go to dianelefer.weebly.com/ to learn about her novels and short fiction collections, and for links to stories and essays available free online. Diane works with survivors of violent persecution as they begin to heal and rebuild their lives.

Jo-Ann Mapson is the author of 12 novels and a book of stories. She taught in the University of Alaska Anchorage's MFA in Creative Writing Program. Awards include the RUSA and the 2014 Best Book New Mexico-Arizona book awards. She lives outside Santa Fe with her husband and four dogs.

Tara Lynn Masih is a National Jewish Book Award Finalist and winner of a Julia Ward Howe Award for her novel *My Real Name Is Hanna.* She's editor of *The Rose Metal Press Field Guide to Writing Flash Fiction* and founded *The Best Small Fictions. How We Disappear* is her second story collection.

Patricia McConnell is an animal behaviorist, international speaker, and writer who is stupid in love with her dogs, loves flowers, and makes the best strawberry/rhubarb pie you've ever had. You can learn more about her at www.patriciamcconnell.com.

Ellen Meister is a novelist, screenwriter, editor, and book coach. Her eighth novel, *Take My Husband* (Mira/August 2022), is a dark comedy about marriage. It follows her other critically-acclaimed books, including *The Rooftop Party, Love Sold Separately, The Other Life*, and *Farewell, Dorothy Parker.* She lost both her parents to Alzheimer's disease.

Kristine Ong Muslim is the author of nine books of fiction and poetry, translator of nine books from Filipino, and editor of several fiction anthologies. She grew up and continues to live in the Philippines.

Robin Oliveira is the author of three novels and an upcoming fourth. For more than three decades, she has lived on the second mountain on the right as you leave Seattle among bobcats, bear, cougars, coyotes, and a very persistent garter snake. She loves her family and friends, Scotland, Paris, and the San Juan Islands, where she hopes to live out her days staring at sunsets.

Pamela Painter is the award-winning author of five story collections. Her stories have appeared in numerous Flash anthologies and she is a Founding Donor of the Flash Fiction Archive, established in 2020 at the Harry Ransom Center, University of Texas, Austin. Painter's latest collection is *Fabrications: New and Selected Stories* from Johns Hopkins University Press.

Alina Pleskova's writing has been featured in *American Poetry Review, Thrush, Peach Mag, Jewish Currents*, and elsewhere. Her full-length poetry collection, *Toska*, will be published by Deep Vellum in spring 2023. More at alinapleskova.com.

Zalisa Rabin is a psychotherapist living and working in New York City.

Victoria Redel is a first-generation American author of four books of poetry and five books of fiction, most recently *Paradise*. Victoria's work has been widely anthologized, awarded, and translated. She has received fellowships from the Guggenheim Foundation, The National Endowment for the Arts. She teaches at Sarah Lawrence College.

Trish Rodriguez is a writer and editor who is currently the Fiction Editor of *Philadelphia Stories*. She is also a senior prose editor at Typehouse. She teaches in Rosemont College's MFA in Creative Writing Program.

Ethel Rohan is an award-winning essayist, novelist, and short story writer. Her latest book, *In the Event of Contact* (2021), won the Dzanc Books Short Story Collection Prize, the Gold IPPY for Best European Fiction, and the Eric Hoffer Short Story Collection Award. From Ireland, she lives in California.

Kathleen Rooney is a founding editor of Rose Metal Press and a founding member of Poems While You Wait. Her poetry collection *Where Are the Snows* won the 2021 X.J. Kennedy Prize from Texas Review Press, and her novel *From Dust to Stardust* will be published by Lake Union in Fall 2023.

Natasha Sajé's books include *The Future Will Call You Something Else* (Tupelo, 2023); a postmodern poetry handbook, *Windows and Doors: A Poet Reads Literary Theory*; and a memoir-in-essays, *Terroir: Love, Out of Place* (Trinity UP, 2020). She teaches in the Vermont College of Fine Arts M.F.A. in Writing Program.

Susanna Sonnenberg is the author of two memoirs, *Her Last Death* and *She Matters: A Life in Friendships*, both New York Times bestsellers. She lives in Missoula, Montana.

C.J. Spataro directs the MFA in Creative Writing and the MA in Publishing programs at Rosemont College and is a founding partner of *Philadelphia Stories*. She is an award-winning short fiction writer. Her work has appeared in many literary magazines and anthologies including *Taboos & Transgressions, Iron Horse Literary Review, december, Sequestrum,* and *Exacting Clam*.

Jennifer Steil is the author of *Exile Music*, which won Grand Prize in the Eyelands 2020 Book Awards; the Multicultural and Historical novel International Book Awards; and was a finalist for the Lambda Literary Lesbian Fiction Award. Previous books include *The Ambassador's Wife* and *The Woman Who Fell From the Sky*.

An author of sweet, small-town romance, **Wendy Rich Stetson** is no stranger to storytelling. She's a Broadway and television actress, an audiobook narrator, and a mom who joyfully made the leap from reading bedtime stories to writing them. Wendy lives in Manhattan with her family and rambunctious Maine Coon kitty.

Chelsea Stickle is the author of the flash fiction chapbook *Breaking Points* (Black Lawrence Press, 2021). Her second chapbook *Everything's Changing* is forthcoming from Thirty West Publishing House in 2023. She lives in Annapolis, MD with her black rabbit George. Read more at chelseastickle.com and find her on Twitter @Chelsea_Stickle.

Nancy Stohlman is an award-winning author and performer. Her book *Going Short: An Invitation to Flash Fiction*, won a Reader Views Gold Award and her flash novel, *After the Rapture*, is forthcoming in 2023. Her work has been anthologized widely and adapted for both stage and screen. www.nancystohlman.com

Julia Strayer has stories in *Kenyon Review* online, *Cincinnati Review, SmokeLong Quarterly, Atticus Review*, and others, including The Best Small Fictions anthology. She won the *Glimmer Train* Short Story Award for New Writers, and 2022 *New Ohio Review* Fiction Contest. She teaches creative writing at New York University. www.juliastrayer.com

New Zealand writer **Jillian Sullivan's** thirteen books include creative non-fiction, novels and short stories. A grandmother, earth plasterer and environmentalist, her awards include the Juncture Memoir Award in America, and the Kathleen Grattan prize for poetry. Her latest book is the collection of essays, *Map for the Heart—Ida Valley Essays*.

Girija Tropp is a winner of the Boston Review Prize and the Josephine Ulrick Literature Award 2006. She has been published in *AGNI, Best Australian Stories, Fiction International, Mississippi Review, Denver Quarterly, Chimurenga, New World Writing*, and other magazines. She is also a Chinese Medicine practitioner, currently living in Byron Bay, Australia.

Deb Olin Unferth is the author of six books. She lives in Texas.

Liza Gardner Walsh has written 15 books for children and adults. She holds an MFA from Vermont College in Fiction Writing and lives in Camden, Maine with her family.

Cat Warren is the author of the New York Times bestseller *What the Dog Knows: Scent, Science, and the Amazing Ways Dogs Perceive the World*, and of a young readers edition of *What the Dog Knows*. She recently retired from North Carolina State University, where she taught science journalism and creative nonfiction.

Xu Xi 許素細**'s** fifteen books include *This Fish is Fowl: Essays of Being* (2019) and *Monkey in Residence & Other Speculations* (Nov 2022). Indonesian-Chinese Hong Kong native, US immigrant, co-founder Authors at Large and William H.P. Jenks Chair in Contemporary Letters, College of the Holy Cross, Massachusetts.

ABOUT THE PHOTOGRAPHER

Meg Boscov's background in performing arts put her on an artistic journey that continues to focus on storytelling—on discovering and communicating the creative and emotional story in each image. Her award-winning photography has appeared in numerous in-person, print, and web exhibitions, including the Photo Review, the Shanti Arts Still Point Gallery and Quarterly Journal, the Foley Gallery in NYC, the PhotoPlace in Middlebury, VT, and various galleries and art centers in the Philadelphia area. Her book *Hand-in-Hand* pairs her macro-photography with micro-essays, one for each week of the year. She is a graduate of Northwestern University and currently resides in Wayne, Pennsylvania, where she continually finds personal joy and creative energy in her surroundings.

ACKNOWLEDGMENTS

We are blessed to have so many wonderful natural, preserved places in the Philadelphia metro area. Meg is extremely grateful to the following:

Chanticleer Garden, Wayne, PA
Jenkins Arboretum, Devon, PA
Stoneleigh: A Natural Garden, Natural Lands, Villanova, PA

Also, Meg's travels brought her to several other gardens and wilds, including Arizona's Sonoran Desert. Thanks also to Katie Montgomery, and all the fine folks at The Camera Store in Bryn Mawr, PA. For the incredible cover and interior design, huge love and appreciation for Michele Charles Barnes. And thank you Laura Ducceschi for the above photograph of the photographer. Meg would like to give a very special thanks to her mother and photographer Eunice Boscov for her inspiration, support, and artistic eye.

Matter Press thanks all the amazing writers who participated in this project. Thanks for your authenticity, artistry, and healing visions.